ANDREW LLOYD WEBBER'S

Aspects of Love

MUSIC BY ANDREW LLOYD WEBBER
LYRICS BY DON BLACK & CHARLES HART
BASED ON THE NOVEL 'ASPECTS OF LOVE' BY DAVID GARNETT

ALEX PLAYED BY MICHAEL BALL
ROSE PLAYED BY ANN CRUMB
GEORGE PLAYED BY KEVIN COLSON
GIULIETTA PLAYED BY KATHLEEN ROWE MCALLEN
JENNY PLAYED BY DIANA MORRISON

A Really Useful Group Publication

Exclusive distributors:

Music Sales Limited
8/9 Frith Street, London W1V 5TZ, England.

Hal Leonard Publishing Corporation
7777 W. Bluemound Road, P.O. 13819 Milwaukee, Wisconsin 53213.

This book © Copyright 1989 & 1990 by
The Really Useful Group plc
Order No. RG10120 ISBN 0.7119.1923.2

Book design & layout by Mike Bell.
Artwork concept by Dewynters Limited, London.
Arranged by Roger Day & Laurence Roman.
Typeset by Capital Setters, London W1.
Music engraved by Music Print Limited.
Photographs by Clive Barda (reproduced by kind permission of
The Really Useful Theatre Co. Limited).
Use of 'Aspects of Love' text reproduced by kind permission of
Aurum Press and The Hogarth Press.
World Premiere at The Prince Of Wales Theatre, London,
Monday April 17th 1989.
Produced by The Really Useful Theatre Co. Limited.

'Alors, je te laisse ... on dirait que French actor as, Rose affectionate together at the ca was still falling on the bo away re

h som oppos him w her sto

indi ent projected Doll's Hous performances a Albi for another young actors an borrowed two th Paul; Marcel had a a fortnight on four was impossible. T to Paris and as sh them, she She would have t

Soi tille avec the fat e tapped left them rain ps

nylon

sly the Builder, The end after only six open their week at mpany of earnest nded. Rose had the leading actor wo, but to live for get herself to Albi ng back th all of money. nd when the rain

LOVE CHANGES EVERYTHING

Love,
love changes everything:
hands and faces,
earth and sky.
Love,
love changes everything:
how you live and
how you die.

Love
can make the summer fly
or a night
seem like a lifetime.

Yes, love,
love changes everything:
now I tremble
at your name.
Nothing in the
world will ever
be the same.

Love,
love changes everything:
days are longer,
words mean more.
Love,
love changes everything:
pain is deeper
than before.

Love will turn your world around,
and that world
will last for ever.

Yes, love,
love changes everything,
brings you glory,
brings you shame.
Nothing in the
world will ever
be the same.

Off
into the world we go,
planning futures,
shaping years.
Love
bursts in, and suddenly
all our wisdom
disappears.

Love makes fools of everyone:
all the rules
we make are broken.

Yes, love,
love changes everyone.
Live or perish
in its flame.
Love will never,
never let you
be the same.

PARLEZ-VOUS FRANÇAIS?

Parlez-vous français?
Je suis sad.
Parlez-vous français?
I feel bad.

How do you say
"ce soir vous êtes
si belle"?

I only know
a word or so,
like "cat" and "school" –
je suis fool.

Parlez-vous français?
Please say "oui".
Parlez-vous français?
Speak to me.

'Well, Mademo— ...vered most of the questions I came ... speaking for the first ti... Englis...

...old J... Alexis, still in the sam...

...y worried … so I thought out of co... come down and put things straight...

'I have a lot to ... you are here there ...

Alexis reappea... sses and hugging bottles.

'Chambéry verm... porto?' he asked.

'Porto is wh... Ros...

'Chamb... ss and gave it to him and filled a gl... e for himself.

'Now, my dear ... it all started,' his uncle asked him ... tone and then suddenly added: ... any misunder-stan... ough... ooked a room for myself... Hôte... nt to be de trop. I shall take myself o...

How do you say,
"vous êtes jolie,
mam'selle"?

Chérie,
where do I commencer,
if you won't parler français
with me?

Parlez-vous français?
Say you do!
Parlez-vous français?
Tell me true!

How do you say
"Je suis unhappy
fella"?

Chérie,
adieu to drinks and danser,
if you won't parler français
with me.

Unless you say "oui" …
adieu to drinks and danser
if you won't parler français
with me.

SEEING IS BELIEVING

Seeing is believing,
and in my arms I see her:
she's here,
really here,
really mine now –
she seems at home here . . .

As his uncle said
'I didn't expect ... sic until after she
had gone. I thoug... ... charge ... rent

'What I really w... ...not to do with the
money part of it – ... on here until she's
due to go to Albi. ... housand francs
and nowhere to go ... will have to get
a lodging in a ghas... ... herself.'
...s voice ... er of fact in telling
...hook w... med unable to go

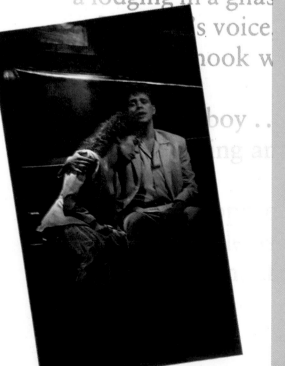

Seeing is believing.
I dreamt that it would be her:
at last
life is full,
life is fine now . . .

Whatever happens,
one thing is certain:
each time I see
a train go by,
I'll think of us,
the night, the sky
forever . . .

He's young,
very young,
but appealing –
I feel I know him . . .

Seeing is believing,
and I like what I see here.
I like
where I am,
what I'm feeling . . .

...boy ... ourse I should not
...ing an... George sounded
down from Paris
not going to, it's
... If you'll excuse

'Damn him for __ said to himself b__ Rose had bro__ latter had __ Next __ unclou__ moment__ passion__ laughing at Alexis__ the twinkling of a__ and declare that A__ her fault. She was__

Alexis could n__ made up his m__ unendurabl__ Rose disapp__ becoming a__ town to go t__

Next mo__ while she w__

'Get up; __

'What do__ upright.

'We are ta__

'See the P__ the window__

'You are__ a horse.'

'Whe__

'Yesterd__ imaginative boy.'

'Darling, __ goodness ...

__ one. Rose was at __ ldenly burst out __ ing him. Then, in __ erself on the head __ was all __ character.
__ essed her, b__ e __ h day would __ e afternoon __ when he was __ een into the __ coffee __ sitting bolt __ y well out of __

What are we doing?
Can you believe it?
A starving actress and
a star-struck boy —
oh well, I might
as well enjoy
the moment . . .

Whatever happens,
we have this moment.
Who needs tomorrow,
when we have today?
Tonight we'll mean
the things we say
forever.

Seeing is believing!
My life is just beginning!
We touched,
and my head won't stop spinning
from winning
your love!

CHANSON D'ENFANCE

Pas de tendresse
et pas de joie,
loin d'ici,
loin de toi.

Rien de plus triste
que mes soupirs,
lorsque vient le jour
où il me faut partir.

Chanson d'enfance,
tu vis toujours dans mon coeur.
Toi, la plus douce!
Toi, la plus tendre!

OTHER PLEASURES

Other pleasures,
and I've known many . . .
Afternoons
in warm Venetian squares,
brief encounters,
long siestas . . .
Pleasures old and new
can't compare with you.

You amaze me!
Where did you come from?
You do things
champagne could never do.
Crystal winters,
crimson summers . . .
Other pleasures –
I would trade them all
for you.

Pleasures old and new
can't compare with you . . .

Wild mimosa,
the scent of evening,
shuttered rooms
with sunlight breaking through,
crazy soirées,
lazy Sundays . . .
Other pleasures –
I would trade them all
for you.

Sailing off
in the night
on a silver lake . . .
Taking more
from this life
than I ought to take . . .
Other pleasures –
I would trade them all
for you.

MERMAID SONG

I am a mermaid
with golden hair . . .
I've never seen one like you!

Not all us mermaids
have silver tails –
I have no tail at all.

*Well I've never
seen any mermaids
with knobbly knees!
I'd say this tale
was a touch too tall,
maybe a touch too tall.*

Sailors would smash on
my jagged rock,
lured by my siren's song.

*It isn't the
song of the siren
that tortures men –
that's where your theory
goes sadly wrong,
that's where it all goes wrong.*

I thought you'd know better.
You know nothing
about mermaids.

to have lunch wi... ...taurant. It would
have been a pleas... ...relationship, but
Alexis said he h... ...would be ridiculo...
the hope that Ro...
an end between th...
to renew relation...
so. Yet he knew...
afternoon and...
would be out...
her. Why, he aske...
uncertainty, this t... ...on?

Alexis had e... ...with women and
friendships with... ...seen Rose, but he
had not felt for a... ...e agitation which

*You know nothing
about sailors.*
I do!
much more than you!
*If you were a sailor
and heard my song,
would you be lured by me?*

I wouldn't be
foolish enough to
go near your rock –
I'd steer my galleon out to sea . . .
lonely and lost at sea . . .

a dirty hall with... ...tury staircase into
which a ram... ...erted. Alexis was
in a state... ...doing at last what
six years before... ...mpted to do but
which, when the... ...ed, he had always

THE FIRST MAN YOU REMEMBER

I want to be
the first man you remember,
I want to be
the last man you forget.
I want to be
the one you always turn to,
I want to be
the one you won't regret.

May I be first
to say you look delightful?
May I be first
to dance you round the floor?
The very first
to see your face by moonlight?
The very first
to walk you to your door?

Well young man, I'd be delighted!
There is nothing I would rather do!
What could be a sweeter memory
than sharing my first dance with you?

I want to be
the first man you remember . . .
The very first
to sweep me off my feet.
I want to be
the one you always turn to . . .
The first to make
my young heart miss a beat.

Seems the stars are far below us.
The moon has never felt like this before.
Our first dance will be forever.
And may it lead to many more.

I want to be
the first man you remember . . .
The very first
to sweep me off my feet.
I want to be
the one you always turn to . . .
The first to make
your young heart miss a beat.

The very first . . .
The very first . . .

bedroom. It was _____ ould not find the switch.

Next moment _____ ge bedroom ____ as _____ nak _____ a _____ caught over the _____ e's naked limbs as _____ exis went in and, _____ Alexis. 'But I don't _____ beautiful with a _____ one eye. Though _____ completely occup _____ ether there was a spark of life left, A _____ ir in Rose's tawny fleece. He had nev _____ She had picked _____ her _____ body under the a _____ so that her powerful shoulder

She watched w _____ Alexis broke the capsule under Sir _____

'There's no pul _____ k he is breathing. Give me your mirr _____

Rose picked up _____ watched silent _____ while Alexis held i _____

'I supp _____ ere _____ would b _____ body ov _____

'I can _____ to him.

HAND ME THE WINE AND THE DICE

poem about the ⟨…⟩ the last lines of
which I shall rea⟨…⟩ thinking of that
poem that led hi⟨…⟩ his friends. I
shall read it in ⟨…⟩nslation, for the
majority of you h⟨…⟩

George was an original man.
He did not want to change human life.
He rejoiced in the way we are made.
He did not look forward to heaven –
he was happy with the earth.
He loved and understood
the flesh, food, wine, love . . .
He lived for today and firmly believed:

lover of poetry an⟨…⟩

'Without more ⟨…⟩ a translation of
Giulietta's speech ⟨…⟩mmitted to heart.
When he had finis⟨…⟩⟨…⟩tences of his own.
His words were ⟨…⟩ect simplicity; he
seemed to be spe⟨…⟩ every word was

If death were given a voice,
that voice would scream through the sky:
live while you may, for I am coming . . .

So . . .

Hand me the wine and the dice,
I want my carnival now,
while I have thirst and lust for living!
So gather all you can reap,
before you're under the plough –
the hand of death is unforgiving!

Alexis half-fill... ...he barrel and then they walked ... ...where he had left his car. It was ... ...ouse and nobody could see them dr...

When Alexis rang ... ...on the following day... ...she said nothing and did ... ...Vincent were sitting at the bre... ...ng-gowns. Marcel was there too.

'I came ... ...and find you still havin...

R... ...a... ...s a change... her.

'Have a glass ... ...just getting to that stag...

'I'll be ready i... ...the room.

'What have yo... ...sked Rose.

'Nothing so fa... ...r the mulber... ...room where...

Vince...

'*Trincquet*,' he...

'Well, I'm wor... ...at's a fact,' said Ro...

'I do... ...tuation in my o...

'You m...

Hand me the wine and the dice,
while there are grapes on the vine –
life is a round of endless pleasures!
The end is always in sight,
but it tastes better with wine –
why pour your life in tiny measures?

Hand me the wine and the dice,
the time is racing away –
there's not a taste that's not worth trying!
And if tomorrow it ends,
I won't have wasted today –
I will have lived when I am dying!

Hand me the wine and the dice,
I want my carnival now,
while I have thirst and lust for living!
So gather all you can reap,
before you're under the plough –
life is a round
of flesh, food, wine, love . . .

ANYTHING BUT LONELY

Anything but lonely,
anything but empty rooms.
There's so much in life to share –
what's the sense when no-one else is there?

Anything but lonely,
anything but only me.
Quiet years in too much space –
that's the thing that's hard to face,
and . . .

You have a right to go,
but you should also know
that I won't be alone for long.
Long days with nothing said
are not what lie ahead –
I'm sorry but I'm not that strong.

Anything but lonely,
anything but passing time.
Lonely's what I'll never be,
while there's still some life in me,
and . . .

I'm still young, don't forget,
it isn't over yet –
so many hearts for me to thrill.
If you're not here to say
how good I look each day,
I'll have to find someone who will . . .

Anything but lonely,
anything but empty rooms.
There's so much in life to share –
what's the sense when no-one else is there?

LOVE CHANGES EVERYTHING

Music by Andrew Lloyd Webber
Lyrics by Don Black & Charles Hart

Off _____ in-to the world we go, plan-ning fu-tures, shap-ing years.

Love _____ bursts in and sud-den-ly, all our wis-dom dis-ap-pears.

Love _____ makes fools of ev-ery-one: all the rules we make are

PARLEZ-VOUS FRANÇAIS?

Music by Andrew Lloyd Webber
Lyrics by Don Black & Charles Hart

ie, where do I com-men-cer, if you won't parl-er fran-çais with me?

Parl - ez vous fran - çais? Say you do!

Parl - ez vous fran - çais? Tell me true!

How do you say "Je suis un-hap - py fel-

SEEING IS BELIEVING

Music by Andrew Lloyd Webber
Lyrics by Don Black & Charles Hart

ALEX: Seeing is believing, and in my arms I see her: she's here, really here, really mine now— she seems at home here...

Seeing is believing. I dreamt that it would be her: at last life is full, life is fine now...

Whatever happens, one thing is certain: each time I see a

CHANSON D'ENFANCE

Music by Andrew Lloyd Webber
Lyrics by Don Black & Charles Hart

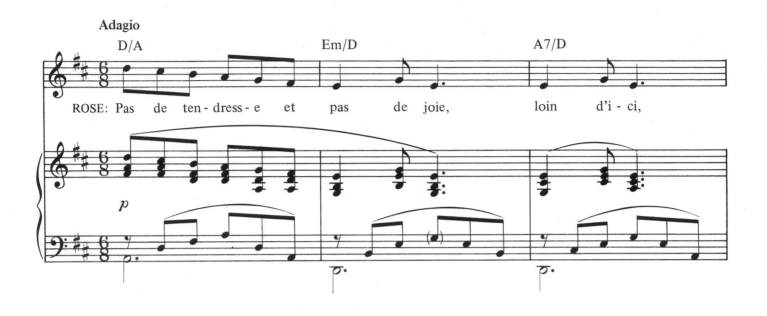

ROSE: Pas de ten-dress-e et pas de joie, loin d'i - ci,

loin de toi. Rien de plus tris - te que mes sou - pirs,

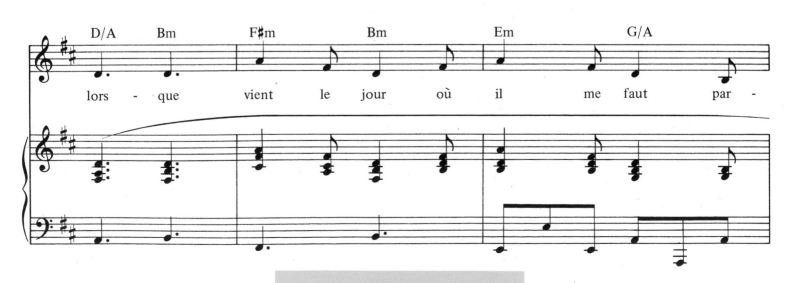

lors - que vient le jour où il me faut par -

OTHER PLEASURES

Music by Andrew Lloyd Webber
Lyrics by Don Black & Charles Hart

Oth-er plea-sures, __ and I've known ma - ny... Af - ter-

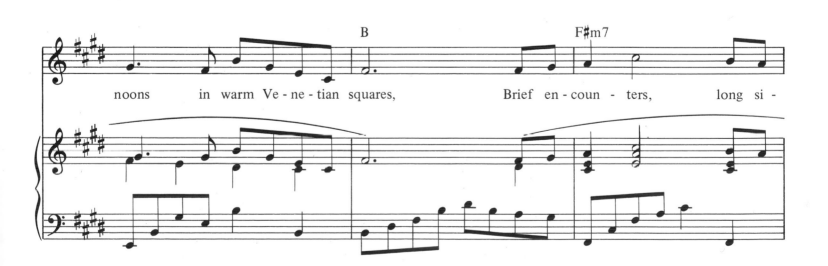

noons in warm Ve - ne - tian squares, Brief en - coun - ters, long si -

Mermaid Song

Music by Andrew Lloyd Webber
Lyrics by Don Black & Charles Hart

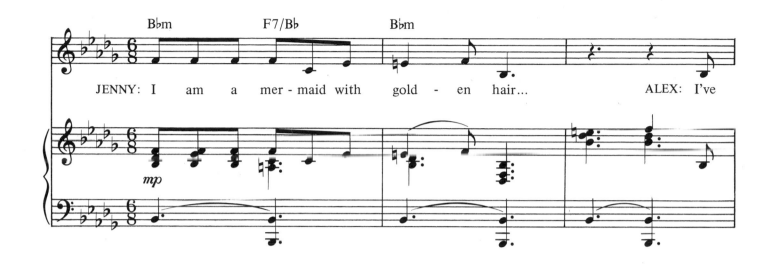

JENNY: I am a mer-maid with gold-en hair... ALEX: I've

ne-ver seen one like you!

JENNY: Not all us mer-maids have
JENNY: Sail-ors would smash on my

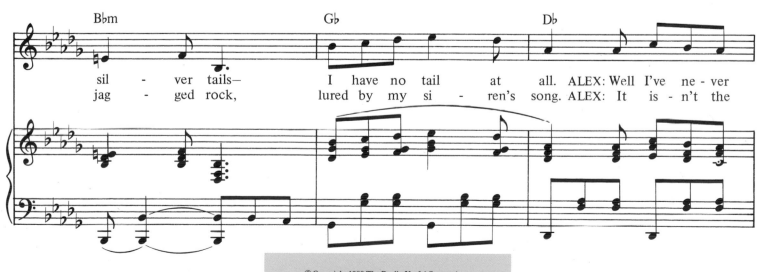

sil-ver tails— I have no tail at all. ALEX: Well I've ne-ver
jag-ged rock, lured by my si-ren's song. ALEX: It is-n't the

The First Man You Remember

Music by Andrew Lloyd Webber
Lyrics by Don Black & Charles Hart

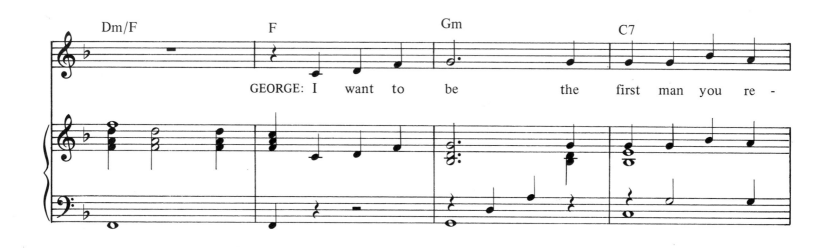

GEORGE: I want to be the first man you re-

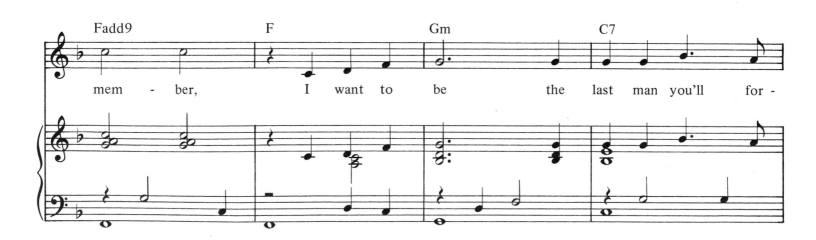

mem - ber, I want to be the last man you'll for -

get.   I want to be   the   one you'll al - ways

turn to, _____ I want to be   the   one you won't re -

gret.   May I be first   to   say you look de -

light - ful? _____ May I be first   to   dance you round the

GEORGE: Seems the stars are far be-low us ____

The moon has ne-ver felt like this be-fore ___

___ BOTH: our first dance will be for -

ev - er. And may it lead to ma-ny more. GEORGE: I

want to be the first man you re - mem - ber ... ___

HAND ME THE WINE AND THE DICE

Music by Andrew Lloyd Webber
Lyrics by Don Black & Charles Hart

GIULIETTA:

George was an o-ri-gi-nal man. __ He did

not want to change hu-man life. He re-joiced in the

way we are made.__ He did not look for - ward to hea - ven— he was

hap - py with the earth.   He loved and un - der-stood the flesh, food, wine, love...

He lived for to - day _____ and firm - ly be - lieved:

If death were gi - ven a voice, __   that voice would

scream through the sky:___ live while you may, for I am

com - ing... ___ So... Hand me the
Hand me the

wine and the dice, ___ I want my car - ni - val now, ___
wine and the dice, ___ the time is rac - ing a - way___

while I have thirst and lust for liv - ing! ___
there's not a taste that's not worth try - ing! ___

48

So ga-ther all you can reap, ___
And if, to - mor-row it ends, ___

be-fore you're un-der the plough–___
I won't have wast-ed to - day–___

the hand of
I will have

To Coda ✛

death is un - for - giv - ing! _____
lived when I am dy - ing! _____

E

Hand me the wine and the dice, ___

while there are

grapes on the vine—___   life is a round of end - less

plea - sures!_____   The end is

al - ways in sight, ___   but it tastes bet - ter with wine—___

why pour your life in ti - ny mea - sures?_____

ALEX: *(Spoken)* George always said, people can have more than one

emotion at the same time. One makes the other

even more acute, then cures it.

CHORUS

Hand me the wine and the dice,___ while there are

grapes on the vine— life is a round of end - less

plea - sures! The end is

al -ways in sight, but it tastes bet - ter with wine—

why pour your life in ti - ny mea - sures?

Hand me the wine and the dice,

I want my car-ni-val now, ___ while I have thirst and lust for

liv - ing! _____ So ga-ther all you can reap, ___

be-fore you're un-der the plough— ___ the hand of

Hand me the wine and the dice, ___ the time is
rac - ing a - way— ___ there's not a taste that's not worth
try - ing!_____ And if to - mor-row it ends, ___
I won't have wast - ed to - day—___ I will have

lived when I am dy - ing! _____

Hand me the wine and the dice, ___ I want my car-ni-val now, ___ while I have thirst and lust for

Anything But Lonely

Music by Andrew Lloyd Webber
Lyrics by Don Black & Charles Hart

ROSE: I hear you're leav-ing us, our lives are changing once a-gain. I came to say good-bye. Good luck, come back and see us now and then.

A - ny-thing but lone - ly,
A - ny-thing but lone - ly,

a - ny-thing but emp-ty rooms.
a - ny-thing but on-ly me.

There's so much in life to 'share—
Qui - et years in too much space—

ADDITIONAL SONGS

REVISED EDITION FEATURING 2 EXTRA SONGS

She'd Be Far Better Off With You

Music by Andrew Lloyd Webber
Lyrics by Don Black & Charles Hart

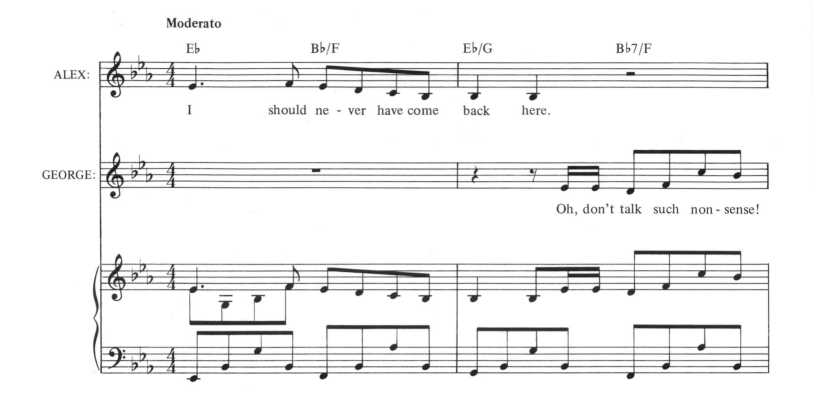

There Is More To Love

Music by Andrew Lloyd Webber
Lyrics by Don Black & Charles Hart

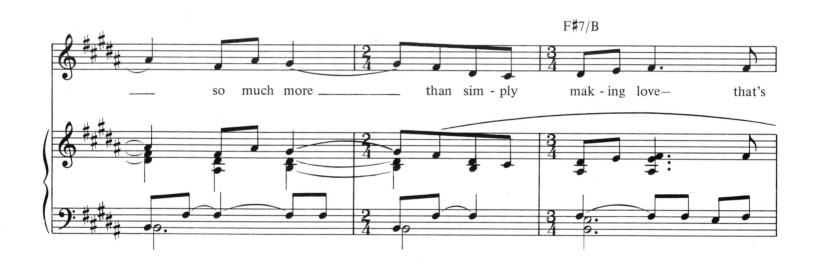

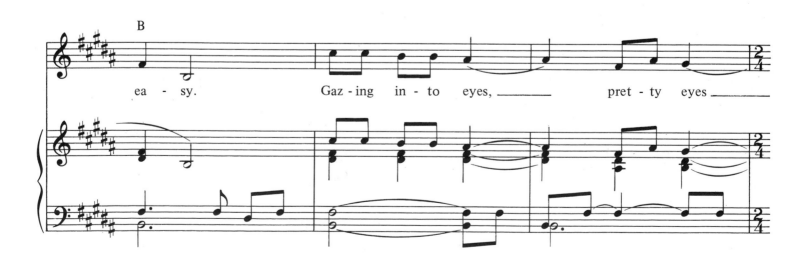

no - thing. There is peace of mind, _____ so much peace _____ in qui - et com - pa - ny— that's some - thing. Ev - ery-one but him _____ seems wrong for me. Ev - ery time I feel _____ there has to be more.

If I could hear _____ the mu - sic I heard then, I'd ne - ver let _____ it fade a - way a - gain.

Now each time love rea - - ches out to me, I can on-ly feel ____ ____ there has to be so much more to love. There is more to love, _____ so much more.

Printed in Great Britain by
Halstan & Co. Ltd., Amersham, Bucks.

8/07 (63000)